GRANDMA, DON'T FORGET

How Much I Love You

LINDA A. GERDNER PhD, RN, FAAN
JACQUELINE A. WITTER EdD, FNP, RN

Illustrator AMY BUNNELL JONES BA

This book is funded by the Richard P. and Edna M. Gerdner Foundation.

Pizzicato Press
Burlington, Iowa

Library of Congress Control Number: 2023920161
Text copyright © 2024 by Linda A. Gerdner and Jacqueline A. Witter
Illustrations copyright © 2024 by Amy Brunnell Jones
Printed in the United States of America

Hardback ISBN: 978-0-9986864-7-9
Paperback ISBN: 978-0-9986864-2-4
E-Book ISBN: 978-0-9986864-8-6

Book design and layout by *the*BookDesigners

Testimonials

Alzheimer's Jamaica located in Kingston, Jamaica is pleased to support the children's and family book, *Grandma, Don't Forget How Much I Love You,* by Linda A. Gerdner and Jacqueline A. Witter. Alzheimer's is an insidious disease that results in behavioral changes and memory loss, leaving families heartbroken, with a lack of understanding for the reason their family member does not remember them.

This story reveals a child's response to the changes she is seeing in her Grandmother Ruby. Too often we do not address the devastating effect this may have on a child. I applaud Linda and Jacqueline for shining light on Alzheimer's disease through the eyes of a child.

—Dundeen Ferguson BA, LLB, CLE
Founder and Executive Director of Alzheimer's Jamaica

My Jamaican heritage has been an instrumental part of my identity. Growing up in the household of my grandma I was influenced by her wisdom, tender heart and generous spirit. I remember the wonderful smells from her kitchen, the jangle of her beads and the vibrant colors of her outfits and makeup. I loved how the characters in this book shared so many sensory connections. It helped ground the story and connected me to my own memories with my grandmother. This book reminds me of our later years together where I cherished our final memories and noted all her parables of wisdom as she was diagnosed with dementia.

As an educator, I am also encouraged by the messages of resilience and family love that will connect to many of my students and their families. The story brings a vibrant energy to a touching story, sharing connections across the senses to the Jamaican culture and an intergenerational love between grandchild and grandmother. Stories such as this are important to the children's literacy canon as they tell an authentic story of family and love, and the all too familiar story of Alzheimer's that crosses all cultures.

All children will benefit from this story of family and learn about Jamaican culture.

—Erin K. Hylton~Dodson MS, MEd
Kindergarten Teacher and Grade Chairperson

This beautifully told and illustrated story is grounded in evidence-based research and practice, but is practical, informative and culturally sensitive. It accurately explores the symptoms, vulnerabilities, stigma, stresses and misperceptions associated with dementia and the intergenerational impact they can have on family. The critical role of family support and understanding is highlighted, illustrating how love and happiness can endure even in the face of a challenging diagnosis like dementia. I highly recommend this book.

—Kathleen C. Buckwalter, PhD, RN, FAAN
Professor and Interim Dean Emerita University of Iowa College of Nursing
Distinguished Professor of Aging Research
D.W. Reynolds Center for Geriatric Nursing Excellence
Oklahoma University Health Sciences Center College of Nursing

Dedication

Jamaica's motto, "out of many, one people," signifies the multiracial heritage and unity of its residents. Alzheimer's disease and related dementias (ADRD) have the potential to affect all persons, regardless of race, culture, and ethnic heritage. However, culture and ethnicity may affect the personal meaning underlying any such chronic illness. This book is dedicated to all of you who know and love someone of Jamaican heritage who has dementia. It was written and illustrated in honor of your individual expressions of culture and ethnic heritage and your dedication to those you love and care for. The purpose is to promote understanding and awareness to foster quality of life.

Acknowledgement

I would like to pay special tribute to my loving parents, Richard and Edna Gerdner, who supported my passion for learning along with the deep desire for understanding persons of various cultures and ethnic groups. Financing through their foundation made this book possible.

Glossary

Gud Mawn': Good Morning.

Mi luv yuh: I love you

Mawnin': Morning

Mi pickney: my child

Oh mi granny! Wen yuh get old di head nuh gud:
Oh your grandma. when you get old your head no good

De olda de moon de britah de shine:
The older the moon the brighter the shine

What a beautiful Saturday morning! Amancia's tummy was full from her breakfast of cornmeal porridge. She skipped toward Grandma Ruby's house, who lived next door. Amancia could smell the sweet scent of flowers lovingly planted by Grandma.

Grandma was softly singing *Blessed Assurance – Jesus of Mine*, while sweeping her yard along with bald patches of red clay earth. Clouds of dust followed the motion of the broom. The singing of colorful birds filled the air, still cool from the night before. Later, the sun would make it too hot to work outside.

Cheerfully, Amancia shouted, *"Gud Mawnin'!*
Mi luv yuh."

Grandma looked up with a wide smile and
shouted, *"Mawnin' mi Pickney."* Calypso
ran toward the road, barking and
wagging his tail.

"Mawnin', Calypso,"
Amancia shouted.

Amancia continued walking to the home of Mrs. Higgons, who was allowing her to pick star apples from her tree – Amancia's favorite! This would be a sweet and refreshing treat for Grandma during her rest period in the hottest part of the day.

When Amancia returned with the juicy, dark purple treasure, Grandma was sleeping in her favorite chair with her Bible resting on her chest. Amancia placed the fruit on the table next to Grandma, where she would see it when she woke-up.

The next morning Amancia and Mother walked from their home to pick up Grandma. Together they walked the clay path to church. Grandma tenderly carried her worn Bible in her wrinkled hands.

While walking, Amancia asked, "Grandma, did you eat the star apple that I placed on the table next to your chair? I picked the best one just for you!"

"I saw no fruit. I ate no fruit. What foolishness!

Amancia shrugged her shoulders and looked puzzled. A long period of silence followed as Amancia's eyes focused on the worn path.

Finally, looking up, she pointed and whispered,
"Look Grandma - a hummingbird."

Grandma's eyes followed the direction of Amancia's finger to
see the shimmering tiny green bird with two long tail feathers.
Grandma whispered, "Yah, a Doctor bird, feeding from the
nectar of a hibiscus flower.

As they approached the old stone church, Amancia focused her attention on the cross perched atop the steeple. As they came closer, she saw the large wooden doors propped open in a welcoming manner. Pastor Miller beamed as he greeted each member of the church.

Upon entering, Amancia and her family sat in their usual spot. Pastor Miller began with an introduction, followed by both the choir and congregation joyfully singing a series of hymns. Grandma's body swayed in rhythm to the music and sang every word of every hymn. Her eyes were sparkling with enthusiasm.

By the time the sermon started, the church was becoming increasingly hot. Women were using hand-held fans to cool their sweating brows. Grandma appeared to be getting very tired; her eyes were less attentive and had lost a bit of sparkle.

Amancia was becoming "wiggly" and felt Mother's elbow gently nudge her. Uh oh, she knew what that meant, but the service was so long...

Following the service, people filed out of church. Amancia spotted the corner of Grandma's Bible peeking out from under the fan. That was odd, Grandma never forgot her Bible.

As they exited, Amancia handed Grandma her Bible. Grandma responded, *"Oh mi granny! Wen yuh get ole di head nuh gud."*

On their way home, the sun was hot and Grandma was walking slower than normal. Amancia became distracted, while briefly talking with a friend from school. When Amancia turned around, Grandma was no longer by her side.

Grandma was about to turn onto a narrow path. Amancia ran toward her and shouted, "Grandma, come this way. That path will take you to the sugar cane fields."

Grandma grumbled, "I have been walking these paths long before you were born. What foolishness!" Amancia gently grasped Grandma's hand while guiding her back on the path that led home.

Mother's thoughts were interrupted by their voices and immediately came rushing over to help. Mother reminded Grandma she had prepared her favorite foods for Sunday dinner. "I made brown stew chicken, rice and peas, and steamed cabbage. We are also having fresh carrot juice and sweet potato pudding for dessert."

Grandma smiled, "That sounds *gud*."

Upon approaching her house, Grandma said, "I would like to go inside for a minute."

Mother asked Amancia to accompany Grandma, while she continued home to finish meal preparation.

Upon entering, Grandma carried her Bible directly to her bedroom and shut the door.

As Amancia walked into the kitchen, something on the counter caught her attention. She walked closer to see. Hmm, the remains of the star apple, it had been there for a while.

Grandma shortly reappeared, without her Bible and church hat. Since she had not changed her clothes, why had she shut her bedroom door? The two then walked to Mother's house.

Upon arrival, they were greeted by the aroma of dinner on the table. Grandma's eyes sparkled when she saw the delicious meal. Amancia was filled with joy as she watched a smile spread across Grandma's face. Based on family tradition, they bowed their heads as Grandma led them in prayer. Between eating bites of food, Grandma was quick to join the family discussion. Grandma seemed like her normal self.

Later, Amancia walked Grandma home and made sure she was safe and settled in her favorite chair.

The next day as Amancia traveled her usual path home from school, she heard shouting from Grandma's home, "Oh Lord help me!"

Amancia ran toward the front door, arriving a few steps ahead of Calypso, leaving him outside as the door slammed shut. Calypso started barking and scratching his paws on the wooden door frame.

Amancia followed the sound of Grandma's voice and found her in the bedroom shouting, "I always keep my Bible next to my bed – it is not here. Someone stole it."

"Grandma, I will help you find it."

Mother heard Grandma's shout from next door. With a pounding heart, she came rushing over. Calypso was at Mother's heels as she ran through the door. Calypso was usually not allowed inside.

Mother found Grandma tossing clothes from her dresser drawers onto the floor. Suddenly, there was a loud thud. Grandma's Bible was lying face down on the floor with pages bent. Grandma grabbed it and clutched it against her chest, "My precious Bible!"

Mother suggested they go into the living room. Calypso followed and protectively sat on the floor, next to Grandma's chair. Grandma continued to clutch her Bible next to her chest, closed her eyes, and tilted her head upward. Spontaneously, she began singing her favorite hymns. She gradually appeared calmer. Amancia stood quietly, and sensed the inner peace that Grandma found by singing hymns.

Suddenly, Grandma heard a whining sound and opened her eyes. She looked down and said, "Calypso, what are you doing in the house?" As she patted him on the head, Calypso jumped up on her lap and began licking her cheek. Grandma began smiling and said, "I love you, too."

Mother said, "He slipped into the house when I opened the door. I think he sensed there was a problem."

Amancia and Mother stayed with Grandma that evening, making sure she was settled in bed and asleep.

Amancia sat on the veranda while troubling thoughts filled her head. She gazed up at the stars and bright full moon, recalling Grandma's words, *"De olda de moon de britah it shine."* She thought about how much she loved Grandma, but Grandma was behaving differently.

Mother joined her daughter on the veranda. Her soothing voice gently broke the silence, "I have been concerned about Grandma. I took her to the doctor today, he thinks Grandma has Alzheimer's disease."

"What is that?" Amancia asked.

Mother explained, "It is a disease that affects the brain. This is the reason Grandma is forgetting things and becoming confused.

"But the doctor can help her, can't he? She will get better, won't she? The doctor helped me, when I broke my arm; he can help Grandma, can't he?

"Well, Grandma's condition is more complicated. There are some medicines that will slow the disease, but none that will cure it. Amancia, Grandma's condition will slowly get worse."

"What are we going to do, Mother?"

"We are going to love her as we always have, maybe even more. We are going to help her when she forgets and becomes confused. We are going to pray for her, and we are going to pray for our own patience and understanding. She will continue to attend church, but we will ride the bus so Grandma doesn't get so tired walking."

"Importantly, we always need to think about Grandma's safety. We are going to continue to evaluate her ability to live alone. For now, she wants to remain in her home. We will take that one day at a time. When that becomes a problem, she will move in with us."

Amancia said, "I have an idea!! Calypso could start spending time in the house with Grandma, to keep her company."

Mother said, "Grandma would like that. I think that is a wonderful idea. Life is much quieter for Grandma since Grandpa died."

Last, Mother said, "I want us to be open with each other. Anytime you have questions or want to talk, I will be there for you. You promise you will do that?"

"Yes Mother, I promise."

The next day after school, Amancia stopped to check on Grandma, who was dozing in a chair on the veranda. Calypso began wagging his tail when he saw her. Amancia leaned over and gently kissed Grandma on her cheek. Grandma opened her twinkling eyes, as a broad smile spread across her face and she began laughing. She wrapped her arms around Amancia and hugged her with all her might. Amancia was filled with love and knew Grandma was also.

Author Notes
Linda A. Gerdner

Alzheimer's disease and related dementias (ADRD) have the potential to affect persons of all races, cultures and ethnicities. It is important to understand that culture and ethnicity may influence the personal meaning underlying the experience of dementia. Individual expression of culture and ethnicity should be honored to accommodate the associated variations of needs.

In this story, Grandma and her family live in Jamaica, with the rich cultural heritage of the Jamaican people embedded throughout the story. For example, the beautiful swallow-tail hummingbird is the national bird of Jamaica, nicknamed "Doctor Bird." Native vegetation is represented in the illustrations. Regional fruits and foods are also incorporated into the daily lives of family members. At times, the Jamaican people may be heard speaking a dialect known as *patois*, as represented in the opening scene.

Early in the story, we see the deep love between Grandma Ruby and Amancia, her granddaughter. The name Amancia means unconditional love, a theme woven throughout this story that is expressed through words and behaviors. As the story advances, Amancia becomes troubled when Grandma begins showing episodes of forgetfulness and confusion. Mother is also concerned about Grandma and schedules a doctor's appointment for her, during the time Amancia is at school. After the doctor has examined Grandma, he decides she likely has Alzheimer's disease. The doctor will monitor Grandma's condition over time.

Dementia has been defined as a group of symptoms associated with a decline in the ability to think, reason, and remember. Dementia is a general term for a variety of diseases that cause these symptoms. However, it is important to have the person seen by a physician to determine the exact cause of these symptoms.

Alzheimer's disease is the most common type of dementia, develops slowly and becomes worse over time. While scientists continue to advance our knowledge about Alzheimer's disease, there is currently no cure.

As Alzheimer's disease advances the person becomes increasingly more vulnerable to stress, causing the person to respond differently to situations, than prior to the disease. In this story Grandma becomes excessively hot as the church service advances and begins showing signs of fatigue. One scene provides somewhat of a parallel, in that Amancia gets "wiggly" as the service progresses and the room temperature increases.

Upon leaving the church, Amancia sees Grandma's Bible and returns it to her. Grandma's response reveals a deep seated misunderstanding and stigma associated with forgetfulness and aging. Although Alzheimer's disease may develop with advanced age, NOT every older or elderly person develops dementia. In addition, dementia is NOT something to be ashamed of. A number of well-known and well-respected Jamaicans have been diagnosed with dementia.

During the family's walk home from church, Grandma becomes increasingly fatigued and hot, leading to confusion. While Amancia and Mother are briefly distracted, Grandma continues walking and is about to turn onto a path leading to the sugar cane field. When Amancia sees this, she begins running and calls out to her. Initially, Amancia attempts to reason with Grandma, but Grandma becomes more determined that she knows the correct path home.

Attempting to reason with a person who has Alzheimer's disease will often cause the person to strengthen their false belief(s).

In contrast, Mother provides a distraction, by telling Grandma of the traditional family meal that awaits them upon their return home. This provides Grandma with the opportunity to focus on something positive. Later, prior to the meal, Grandma maintains her position of honor at the head of the table and leads the family in prayer, by drawing upon her long-term memory.

Safety is a constant concern that must be accessed for persons with dementia. This may require a fine balance to avoid needless restrictions that reduce quality of life. Talk to health professional about these types of decisions. Incorporating meaningful activities from the person's cultural or ethnic background is important. For example, in this story it is important to maintain and support the religious activities that are meaningful to Grandma. These include attending church, reading Bible verses, praying, and singing hymns. This may require some adaptation. For example, Mother suggests the need to begin using public transportation to and from church on Sundays, to reduce the physical stress on Grandma.

Singing hymns remain an important and preserved ability for Grandmother. The opening scene of this story portrays Grandma singing a hymn while sweeping her yard. During church Amancia recognizes Grandma's ability to remember every word of every hymn. During an extremely stressful event, Amancia and Mother arrive to ensure Grandma's safety. Following this crisis, Grandma appears to regain an inner peace by softly singing hymns while family remain near. Language and music are processed in different areas of the brain. Therefore, the person with Alzheimer's disease is often able to process and express music even into the advanced stages of the disease, when no longer able to understand verbal language or spoken words.

In the above mentioned scene Grandma becomes stressed when unable to find her "precious" Bible. She has likely hidden her Bible in a drawer, beneath clothing items, in fear that someone will take it. However, due to impaired short term memory, she forgets she has done this, and believes it has been stolen. Grandma knows where she usually keeps her Bible, but she is unable to remember altering from this location and routine. Change in routine may cause the person to become confused. Grandma has a doctor's appointment that day; although necessary, it does involve a change in her routine. Although not always possible, it is helpful to maintain a regular routine for the person with Alzheimer's disease.

Pets, such as a dog, may provide companionship and unconditional love to persons with Alzheimer's disease. In this story, we see Calypso's protective nature toward Grandma. It is important to see Grandma's joyful response to the expression of love in the final scene of the story.

Persons with Alzheimer's disease are sensitive to nonverbal communication and will sense any negativity felt or expressed by others. Family and friends need to be accepting and non-judgmental. To avoid isolation, older persons should be encouraged to retain friends and family in their social circle. As we learn and show our acceptance, we have the opportunity to teach others. Our purpose in writing this book is to promote this awareness in others through public education.

Other important resources are available to support persons with dementia and their family members. This includes *Alzheimer's Jamaica*, an affiliate of *Alzheimer's Disease International*, a world federation of Alzheimer's Associations.

About the Authors and Illustrator

Linda A. Gerdner PhD, RN, FAAN has dedicated her career to helping persons with Alzheimer's disease and related dementias and the family members who care for them. She has conducted research to explore the perception, meaning and care of dementia within various ethnic groups such as African Americans living in the Arkansas Delta and Hmong Americans living in the Midwest. Most recently she served as an Ethnogeriatric Specialist at the Geriatric Education Center, School of Medicine, at Stanford University. She is widely published and has received national and international awards for her contributions. She pioneered the theory driven evidence-based protocol of Individualized Music for Persons with Dementia. Ethnicity is an inherent criterion in the assessment for this intervention. She is a co-editor of the third edition of the ground breaking book, *Ethnicity and the Dementias* published by Taylor and Francis. This is her third illustrated book for children and family about Alzheimer's disease. Her first, *Grandfather's Story Cloth* (bilingual English/Hmong) was written as a culturally responsive learning resource for the Hmong American community. The second, *Musical Memories,* helps children and their families understand the cause of behaviors associated with Alzheimer's disease and use of music as a means of communication in reducing anxiety and agitation in persons with Alzheimer's disease.

Jacqueline A. Witter EdD, FNP, RN moved from Jamaica, West Indies, to be with her family in New York and she is the youngest of eleven children. Although, leaving her country of birth, she did not depart from her strong upbringing of moral principles, cultural values, beliefs, and love for Jamaican patois. She has over 30 years of nursing experience; expanding from academia, home care, acute care, nursing education, nursing quality and hospital administration. Dr. Witter has received numerous awards for nursing leadership, education and research. She is known nationally and internationally for her work and publications on nurse mentoring, anti-bullying and transition of care for caregivers. Dr. Witter has presented at several conferences in Jamaica: Northern University; Caribbean Nursing Organization 32nd Biennial Conference and the Omega Kappa Chapter. She values the strong family bonds, instilled by her now deceased parents. Her dearly beloved mother had Alzheimer's disease, requiring home care by herself and some of her siblings. This experience served as the inspiration for Dr. Witter's participation in this book. It was the love of their mother and the gift of patience that helped them to endure this experience. It is her hope that this book will bring awareness and enhanced understanding of this disease to children and their families.

Amy Bunnell Jones B.A. was born in Salt Lake City, UT. As a young child, she loved to draw, paint and glue things together. Although her images and sources of inspiration have changed, she still enjoys these art activities. Receiving a B.A. in Art Education from Brigham Young University provided her with the opportunity to try her hand at many different mediums such as stained glass, watercolor, oil, ceramics, plaster, and batik. The only thing she likes as well as creating art is teaching it. While raising five children, she has taught art classes to budding artists of all ages. She is also the illustrator of *The Lifting Balloons* by Erin Hardy Mendes and runs an online business selling her artwork.

Printed in the USA
CPSIA information can be obtained
at www.ICGtesting.com
LVRC090124260124
769712LV00012B/264